Pragya Tales

For

Children

(Part - 2)

Fables based on Pragyapuran and Preachings of

Pandit Shriram Sharma Acharya

By

BRAHMAVARCHAS

First Edition:
2006

English Translation by:
Shri T.N. Sahay

Publishers:
**Shri Vedmata Gayatri Trust
Shantikunj, Hardwar: 249 411**

Tel: 91-1334-260602, 261328, 260403
Fax: 260866
Web: www.awgp.org
Email: shantikunj@awgp.org

Price: 45.00

ISBN No: ISBN-81-8255-018-1

Preface

During the past 79 years, the Gayatri Pariwar Mission has traveled a long way spreading its ideology of resurrection of morality and righteous hinking in global society through dissemination of spiritual disciplines of Gayatri and constructive efforts of mass awakening. Today, it has grown into a grand family of millions of members belonging to different classes, creeds, color, race and faith and residing in different parts of the world.

Behind the spectacular progress of mission's ideology amongst the masses was active participation of thousands of dedicated youth of India.

With its sight on the destined Golden Era of 21st century, foreseen by the seer-sage, Yug Rishi Pandit Shriram Sharma Acharya, the mission has planned to bring out literature on the science of spirituality for the young citizens of tomorrow.

The illuminating literature, motivating teachings and sermons of the Yug Rishi encompasses almost all topics pertaining to happy progress and enlightenment of human life. The present publication "Pragya Tales" is compiled for children based on his inspiring teachings. It is hoped that it will be useful in making the children as responsible citizens in the forthcoming Golden Era of human values.

Dr. Pranav Pandya
Shantikunj, Haridwar

Contents

God Helps Those
Who Help Others

On the bank of a river in a forest there lived many animals. Many amongst the bigger animals could swim easily across the river. On the other hand the smaller ones like rabbits and squirrels did not know swimming. For crossing the river, they took help of a large tortoise living on the bank of the river.

The tortoise was very friendly and polite. He spoke sweetly to everyone. Throughout the day, he helped the small animals cross the river by carrying them on his back. Because of his helping nature, the tortoise had made many friends.

In the neighborhood of the tortoise, there also lived a crocodile and an otter.

The crocodile was very proud, selfish and lazy.

He thought that the smaller animals were inferior to him. He was proud that he could walk faster than the smaller animals. None amongst the tiny animals could move as fast as him for long distances.

He often boasted about his capabilities.

The crocodile was very lazy. While other animals worked, he slept on the bank of the river throughout the day. Those who do not work become fat. The crocodile had become very fat. The other strong animals made fun of his fat body.

He was also very selfish. He never helped anyone. When the small animals on the land desired to go to the other side of the river and asked him to give him a lift, he made excuses and refused to help.

No one wants to be friendly with a person who does not help anyone. Because of his selfish nature the crocodile did not have any friends.

One day, while the otter was swimming in the river, he met the crocodile. The otter was very tired. He thought perhaps the crocodile would help him and give him a lift.

The otter said, "I am very tired. I need some rest. Could you take me on your back to the sandbar in the middle of the river?

The crocodile replied, "I have no time. I am busy in going to the other bank of the river."

The large tortoise swimming nearby also heard the otter speaking to the crocodile.

He called the otter and said, "I can carry you to the sandbar on my back."

The otter climbed on the back of the tortoise and he took him to the sandbar. From that moment, the tortoise and the otter became close friends. Whenever the otter got tired while swimming in the river, the tortoise gave him a lift.

In this way, by helping many other animals the tortoise made many more friends.

Since the crocodile did not have any friend he felt envious of the tortoise. He thought that if he could show other animals that he was superior to the tortoise, everyone would become his friend.

He waited for an opportunity to prove his superiority over the tortoise. One day he challenged the tortoise to compete with him in a race. The tortoise knew that because of his smaller body, he could not defeat the crocodile in a race.

The tortoise said, "How can I compete with you in a race on land? You are much bigger than me. You can also run faster than me. However, since both of us know swimming I am prepared to compete with you in a race in the river."

The crocodile was very cunning. He knew that the tortoise could swim fast in the river. He could not swim faster than the tortoise.

He thought of a clever way to defeat the tortoise.

The crocodile knew about a place in the river, which had many whirlpools.

He thought if he asked the tortoise to cross the river at that place, he would not be able to swim through the whirlpools easily. While trying to go across the whirlpools the tortoise would become tired, whereas because of his large size and strength he would easily go through them.

Through the whirlpools, he will be able to reach the other bank across the river earlier than the tortoise and would win the race.

Next morning all animals gathered on the bank of the river to watch the swimming race between the tortoise and the crocodile.

With all animals on the bank of the river waiting eagerly for the result, the race began.

The crocodile and the tortoise entered the river and began to swim towards the other bank. When they had traveled for some distance, the level of the river suddenly rose on account of a flash flood in the area upstream.

Heavy rainfalls had risen up the water-level of the river.

Persons who do hard physical work do not get tired easily. Since the crocodile did not have the habit of working hard, and was mostly sleeping throughout the day, he got tired.

He felt that he could not swim as fast in the swift current of the flooded river.

However, it did not worry the crocodile.

The crocodile felt confident that he could win the race even if he waited for the water level to subside and started later than the tortoise.

Because of his habit of sleeping during the daytime, he felt sleepy. He thought since he could swim faster than the tortoise he had enough time for a short nap. He returned back to the starting place and fell asleep on the bank of the river.

In the meantime, the tortoise continued to swim towards the other bank of the river. His habit of working hard had made him strong. He did not feel any difficulty in swimming in the swift current of the river.

A little away from the tortoise, the otter was also swimming. The otter saw him and asked the reason for his hurry.

The tortoise said, "The crocodile has asked me to compete in a race across the river. The finishing point is that banyan tree on the other bank. I think the crocodile has gone ahead of me. I don't know how to catch up with the crocodile Because of the swift current, I cannot swim faster."

The tortoise did not know that the crocodile had gone back to the starting point, but the otter had seen him sleeping there.

The otter said, "You need not worry. The tortoise has gone back and is still there at the starting place of the race. He is waiting for the level of the river to subside."

Where is the finishing post of the race?"

Pointing out at the banyan tree right across the river, the tortoise replied, "We are competing to reach that tree. Whoever reaches there will become the winner."

The otter was familiar with all parts of the river.

He said, "Dear friend you cannot swim across in that part of river. There are big whirlpools ahead, which you will not be able to cross. I know of one

more course for crossing the river. However it is too long. If you follow that course you may get tired.

Besides, the bank of the river on that course is a little away from the banyan tree.

Nevertheless, do not lose heart. I will show you the way to reach the tree from that part of the bank. After crossing the river, you will be able to go to the tree by talking on the bank besides the river. You need not go through the whirlpools.

Since the otter knew about the sandbar in the middle of the river he asked he tortoise to accompany him to the sandbar.

On reaching the sandbar, he told the tortoise, "You may take rest here and

MORAL

God sends someone to help the person who helps others in their need.

wait for the current of the river to slow down. Then you may resume the race and reach the finishing post earlier than the crocodile."

The tortoise followed the advice of his friend otter. As soon as the level of water in the river fell down and current became slower, he paddled fast to cross the river.

In the meantime, the crocodile suddenly woke up from his slumber. He was startled to see the tortoise close to the other bank of the river. He immediately jumped into the river and began to swim fast.

However, before the crocodile could reach the middle of the river, the tortoise had already reached the winning post at the banyan tree. His nature of helping others in need has helped him find a friend, who helped him in his ours of need.

God sends someone to help the person who helps others in their need.

The Father
Son and a Horse

An old man had bought a new horse. He and his son often traveled on this horse to visit the neighboring village. One day he decided to go with his son on a long journey to a place far from his village.

Since the man was going on a long journey, he was not sure whether the horse could carry both of them over long distances. Hence, being old, while he himself rode the horse, he asked his son to walk besides him.

On the way, they came across a young man. The young man commented "This man does not love his son. He is mounted on the horse and is making the poor young son walk on foot."

On hearing this, the old man dismounted and asking his son to ride, began to walk besides the horse.

A little ahead on their way, an old woman saw them and criticized the son "How cruel and disrespectful is this young boy? He is riding the horse and making his old father walk."

The earlier comment of the young man and the words of this old woman confused the old man and his son.

They thought it was proper for both of them to ride together. Then it would create an impression that they cared for each other.

The son requested his father to sit behind him on the horse. In this way both proceeded on their journey riding the horse together.

After some time they crossed a village. Near a large stable in the village a few men were seated. Their horses were fastened besides the stable.

In order to give their horse some rest, the man and his son got down from the horse and to quench its thirst, led it to a sink of water near the stable.

After the horse had taken water, both began to mount it again for continuing their journey. However, watching the two persons sitting on the horse together, the men sitting around the stable began to laugh.

One of the men came near to them and said, "Why are you torturing the poor horse by riding it together? You are loading it with too much of weight.

The son said, "You are right. We did not notice that the weight of both of us was too much for the horse to carry. Now onward we shall give the horse rest by leading it without a rider."

Saying it, both of them dismounted and began to walk with the horse following them close behind.

When they had gone a little further, they came across one more group of men.

Seeing the man and his son walking with a horse without a rider, they too began to laugh.

One amongst the men commented, "How foolish these two persons are? In spite of having a horse they are walking on foot?"

The man and his son felt very much confused. What were they expected to do with their horse?

In the beginning of their journey, when they rode the horse one by one, the young man and the old woman told that they did not love each other. Later when they rode it together, people complained that there was too much load on it. Finally when they decided to take the horse without a rider, then too people considered them foolish for not riding the horse.

Further ahead on their way, there lived a sage. The man decided to seek his advice.

On meeting the sage, he narrated the sequence of events.

He said, "Sir! People make fun of us when we ride the horse singly, one at a time, together, or even go on foot without riding. What are we supposed to do?"

The sage told the man, "You should not feel worried about the comments of others. People view things in the light of their own personal experiences.

When you were riding and your son was walking, the young man blamed you for making your son walk on foot. This young man was made to work very hard by his own father without any rest. That is why he had sympathy for your son.

When your son was riding the horse and you were walking, the old woman accused your son for making you walk. This woman herself had a very disobedient and bad tempered son.

Her son did not care for the comforts of his parents. For this reason, this old woman had sympathy for all old persons, who had disobedient children.

The old woman thought that your son was also like her undisciplined son. He was making you walk for his own comfort.

People near the stable, who blamed both of you for loading the horse too much with the weight of two riders, were traders of horses. They noticed

that your horse was too tired to carry the weight of two persons and excess weight was going to make it sick.

The men, who made fun of you for not riding the horse and leading it without a rider, were butchers. They were very cruel towards animals. Hence they did not see anything wrong in a tired horse carrying a heavy load.

Hence, you should not be worried when people pass comments on your work. They speak on the basis of their own personal experiences.

To a thief everyone appears a thief. Wherever a thief goes, he talks only about thievery. His friends and companions also discuss the same subject.

Gentlemen always find some good quality in everyone.

Their comments and discussions are always about goodness in people.

People take interest only in those subjects, which are liked by them. They also easily find friends with similar likings. However, everyone respects you, ignores you or hates you only on the basis of your manners, virtues and vices.
It does not matter, how you look like, what you wear or what worldly things you possess.

Everyone judges you by his own personal experience.

When you go out, the cobbler judges your status by the quality of your shoes and a tailor by the quality of your clothes.

In social gatherings, the fashion designer watches your clothes and hairstyle and the status-conscious person keenly observes the quality of your, clothes, tie, wristwatch, jewelry, and model of your bike, scooter or car.

People take interest only in those subjects, which are liked by them. They also easily find friends with similar likings.

However, everyone respects you, ignores you or hates you only on the basis of your manners, virtues and vices.

It does not matter, how you look like, what you wear or what worldly things you possess.

Hence you should never be worried about the opinions of people around you. When in doubt, use your own wisdom to decide whether you are right or wrong?

13

Hence you should never be worried about the opinions of people around you. When in doubt, use your own wisdom to decide whether you are right or wrong?

It is very easy to know whether you are right or wrong.

If what you think, speak or do is helpful to someone, you are right. If your action hurts someone physically or mentally, you are wrong.

MORAL

You cannot please everybody by your actions. The comments of people reflect their own convictions and impressions. Without caring for "what people would say...", use your own wisdom to judge your actions.

God protects
Those Who do not Harm Others

In a forest near a town there lived many big and small animals. In a small house in the middle of forest there also lived a magician.

The animals were afraid of human beings living in the town. As soon as they saw a man coming closer, they would run away for their safety.

There was a rat living in a small hole dug at the base of a tree in the forest. The rat too was afraid of human beings.

The rat moved out of its house only during the night. When people fell asleep inside their homes, he would come out of his hole and eat the leftover food thrown by people in the garbage outside.

The rat often wondered about the good food taken by human beings. He desired to eat the variety of fresh food prepared by them.

One night, when everyone was asleep, the rat entered a house and stole food kept in the kitchen. He found the food very delicious. He thought that it was easier to get food in the kitchen of people than search for it in the garbage.

He began to go into the houses of people and have a stomach full from the food kept in their kitchen.

Soon, the residents of a house found out about the mischief of the rat. They set up a trap and the rat was caught. They released it in a far away forest.

The rat had to walk a great distance to return to his residence. It made the rat very unhappy. He envied the cats, which could easily enter the homes of people and eat everything without being caught.

The rat went to the magician and said, "Sometimes I do not get anything to eat in the forest. I have to enter the houses of human beings for my food.

People do not let me enter their houses. On the other hand, the cats move in the houses of people without any fear of being caught.

Could you change me into a cat?"

The magician agreed to the request of the cat. He waived his magic wand and changed the rat into a cat.

For a few days this cat felt very safe and happy. Now she could go anywhere without fearing man. It could climb up the trees, walk on the walls and fences and eat whatever it found.

One day, this cat spotted a small cub of a bear in the jungle. The mother of the cub had gone away to drink water, leaving the cub alone.

The cub was very small. At the time of birth, the baby-bears hardly weigh a kilogram but when they grow up as adult, their weight increases to more than a quintal.

Finding the cub without its mother, the cat caught the cub by the neck and climbed up a tree to eat it.

In the meantime the mother bear returned.

Bears have a strong sense of smell. Sniffing all the way, the mother bear followed the trail of the cat and reached the tree. Since the trail of smell came to an end at the base of the tree, the bear stood up to look up at the tree in search of her missing cub.

While standing erect on its hind legs, a bear appears very frightful. The height of a bear standing erect can be up to three meters. The body of the bear was as large as a big car.

The sight of the large bear frightened the cat. With the cub of the bear in her mouth, she climbed further up on the tree. The mother bear hugged the thick trunk of the tree with its long limbs and powerful paws, and began to climb up behind the cat.

To escape the bear, the cat kept going up and up till it reached the top of the tree.

Looking down from the top of the tree, the cat saw the big bear slowly coming up towards it. However, having reached the top, the cat could go no further to save herself from the bear.

The cat saw a branch of the tree extending at right angles to the trunk of the tree. She crawled on this branch and went to its furthest end.

In the meantime, climbing the tree the bear also reached where the branch came out of the trunk of the tree.

However, the bear could not move on the branch. The branch was not sufficiently strong to support the heavy body of the bear.

Holding the trunk of the tree with both front legs, the bear stopped climbing and looking angrily towards the cat began to growl angrily.

The angry grunts of the bear and its bloodshot eyes terrified the cat.

The tree was about twenty feet tall. From this great height, the cat could not jump down without getting hurt.

On the other hand, with the bear at the other end of the branch it could neither climb down.

For a long time, both animals waited for the other to move. For the cat, there was no place to go and the bear had no intention of going away without its cub.

In this way several hours passed. The cat had not eaten anything since long. It was also feeling sleepy and thirsty. Trembling with fright, it dropped the cub held in her mouth. It fell down with a thud on a big heap of leaves at the base of the tree. The cushion of leaves saved the cub from getting hurt. God had so nicely saved it!

Falling on the ground, the cub cried for his mother.

The sound of the cub drew the attention of the mother bear. It looked down and finding his cub there, climbed down the tree. On reaching the ground, the bear sniffed the cub. Finding it unhurt, it picked the baby softly in its mouth and, walked away, forgetting the cat on the tree.

The cat had learnt a lesson. As a rat, it had been punished earlier for stealing food. It had to face a problem again because of the habit of stealing.

The cat wondered if it could eat fruits like monkeys, it did not have to steal for food. There were many trees with fruits on them. If it were a monkey it could eat fruits and would not require stealing meat or food from other animals and human beings.

The cat also thought that becoming a monkey it would grow very strong by eating fruits and vegetables.

It had observed that the vegetarian elephant was the strongest animal in the forest and had a long life. Eating only fruits and vegetables, the monkeys too were very active.

Throughout the day they jumped up and down the trees without getting tired.

On the other hand, sometimes the non-vegetarian animal food often spoiled its stomach.

19

Hence the cat decided to request the magician to change itself into a monkey.

The cat told the magician, "Sir! Please change me into a monkey, so that I may eat fruits and vegetables to become strong and active."

The magician again moved his magic stick and the cat became a monkey.

As monkey the cat felt very happy. It jumped from one branch of tree to another, eating all types of delicious fruits and vegetables.

However, by eating fruits and vegetables of a variety of tastes throughout the day, the monkey became greedy. Now it desired to eat even when the stomach was full. It would enter the houses of people and steal the food kept in their homes.

One, who troubles others, is not tolerated for long. People complained to the officers of the civil

One, who troubles others, is not tolerated for long.

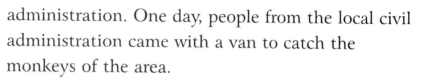

administration. One day, people from the local civil administration came with a van to catch the monkeys of the area.

In order to escape being caught, the monkey fled and hid in a dry well.

It again went to the magician and requested him to change itself back into the rat.

By now it had realized that whenever it stole food, it had to face problems.

The magician said: "I hope with your experience as a rat, cat and monkey, you have learnt that whoever you are, and wherever you live, you have nothing to fear unless you do something to trouble others".

MORAL

God protects the helpless innocents. Those who speak or act to harm others have to face problems.

21

The Result of
Mockery

Sahasrapad took pleasure in mocking and teasing people. He had a friend named Kandarbha.

Kandarbha had practiced great yogic exercises and meditation for many years. It had given him many supernatural powers. However he had an inherent fear of snakes.

One day, Sahasrapad threw a creeper at Kandarbha and shouted that a snake had fallen on his shoulders from the overhanging branch of a tree.

It frightened Kandarbha so much that he fainted because of the shock.

On regaining his senses, he expressed his anger by cursing Sahasrapad to be born as a serpent in his next birth.

The curse of an achieved saint never goes waste. In his next birth, Sahasrapad had to live as a snake.

Sahasrapad had to pay a heavy penalty for playing a prank on a saintly person.

The Insult, Which Started
A Great War

Yudhisthir, the eldest brother amongst the five Pandavas, lived in a magnificent palace with his younger brothers and wife Draupadi. This palace had miraculous architectural features. Experts had built in it many features of optical illusion.

In this palace there were invisible partitions, solid floors laid with marbles creating an illusion of water filled tanks and pathways appearing like canals.

Once Yudhishthir invited their cousin Duryodhan, the son of the blind king Dhritrashtra of Hastinapur.

The glitter and grandeur of the palace envied Duryodhan. The design of the shining floor and walls created a sort of visual illusions in his sight. While walking in the palace he collided against an invisible glass like partition and fell into a tank, which appeared like solid floor.

It amused Draupadi. Whispering with a laughter she made a comment, saying, "There goes the blind son of the blind father."

It made Duryodhan very angry. He returned back to his palace with the resolve to avenge the insult.

One day, he invited the Pandava brothers to participate with him in a game of Chausar. (Chausar was an indoor gamble like dice-game in ancient times in which small shells were used as dice.)

Winning each stake by trick Duryodhan made the Pandava brothers lose all their money. When nothing was left with them, he persuaded the Pandavas to put their wife Draupadi at stake.

Gambling is a very bad habit. While gambling, in the chase of 'winning in the next chance' a gambler loses all sense of right and wrong and continues with whatever he is challenged to put at stake.

In their final 'hope' to win the game, the Pandvas put their wife Draupadi at stake.

The Pandavas lost this final stake as well and Draupadi was left to the mercy of cruel Duryodhan.

Duryodhan asked his brother Dushasan to undress Draupadi in full view of courtiers.

With tears in her eyes Draupadi pleaded to the senior members of the court and relatives to save her from the shame. But because of the terror of

Duryodhan, none dared speak a word.

Dushasan began to pull the Sari in which Draupadi was draped. In desperation she clutched the sari tightly against her body, but Dushasan was too strong to resist. Finally, finding herself totally helpless, she raised her hands in the air and prayed to God to come for her rescue.

God does not disappoint the devotee who totally surrenders to HIM. So long, Draupadi depended on her own self by holding the sari with her hands,

If one TOTALLY surrenders to God and earnestly prays for help, HE comes to rescue immediately.

MORAL

One should never insult anyone even casually. The result of insulting may bring dangerous consequences for the person.

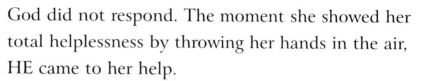

God did not respond. The moment she showed her total helplessness by throwing her hands in the air, HE came to her help.

God made the length of Draupadi`sari endless. Dushasan kept on pulling it for hours, but could not undress the lady. Tired and scared, he finally gave up.

Bhim, the husband of Draupadi then took a resolve to kill Dushasan and Duryodhan.

Thus a casual insulting comment of Draupadi became the root cause of the great war of Mahabharat.

27

Association with a Dishonest Person
Makes one Dishonest

The great war of Mahabharat had come to an end. The Kauravas were defeated. Their commander- in - chief, Bhishma was deeply wounded.

Bhishma was a great yogi .He had been blessed with the power to choose his own moment of death. He desired to discard his physical body during a holy configuration of solar system.

As a true warrior, Bhishma preferred to die in the battlefield itself. On his request, Arjun the great warrior amongst the Pandavas, had prepared a bed for him by shooting a carpet of arrows in the earth.

In those days, soldiers fought only between sunrise and sunset during the day. The beginning and end

28

of the battle of the day was announced by blowing conch shells by the commander-in chief of the opponent armies.

Enmity was being kept confined only to the duration of war in the battlefield. After the end of the battle of the day, soldiers visited each other's camps, nursed the wounded and offered condolences for the dead.

The daily routine of discussions on spirituality was maintained even during the war. People attended the discourses of scholars of spirituality in both camps, irrespective of the army they belonged to.

Bhishma was a renowned scholar of Vedic Scriptures. Knowing that he was going to die soon, Krishna asked Yudhishthir, the eldest amongst the Pandva brothers, to learn the fundamentals of spirituality from Bhishma.

The other brothers and their wife Draupadi also accompanied him.

While the Pandvas were listening to Bhishma`s preaching on morality, Draupadi smiled.

Bhishma inquired, "What has made you smile?"

Draupadi said, "Sir! You are teaching us that an immoral action by anyone should be opposed. If you are so enlightened, why didn't you stop Dushasan from insulting me by trying to disrobe me publicly in the court of Duryodhan?"

Bhishma replied, "When it happened, I was an employee of Duryodhan.

Throughout life Duryodhan had been dishonest in all his activities. Dishonesty had entered into everything associated with him.

I stayed in his palace, ate the food and used all the facilities granted by him, everything there was polluted with dishonesty. So, the evil effects had entered into depths of my mind and weakened me too. That is why I did not dare stop the shameful behavior of Dushasan.

MORAL

Close association with immoral persons in any way makes man immoral.

The war is over. All my dirty blood soaked with immoral effects has flown. The wounds I have voluntarily taken on my body are my penance. Now I am a free man. I am no longer an 'employee' of Duryodhan. Now, I repent, why I did not stop Duryodhan and Dushasan from insulting you.

The scriptures say that, everything associated with an immoral person becomes polluted with sin. If one uses something belonging to such a person, the mind of the user also becomes sinful. Therefore one should not accept any favor from a sinful person.

My own experience has confirmed that one cannot behave morally if one depends upon a dishonest person or takes food offered by him.

Misuse of Power
Destroys its User

Bhasmasur performed extreme ascetic yoga sadhana for years to please god Shiva. He wanted to become the most powerful person on earth. When Shiva found that he had accomplished the sadhana worthy of receiving a boon, HE appeared before Bhasmasur in person and inquired his purpose.

Bhasmasur requested Shiva to bless him with such power as to burn anyone to ashes by putting his hand on his head.

As per the Law of Nature, Shiva granted him the power because of his devout, arduous sadhana, but warned him that he could use this power only for destroying the evils. He told him that if he used this power for an immoral purpose, this power was going to destroy him.

God blesses extraordinary capabilities to only those persons, who do not become greedy and arrogant upon becoming more powerful and talented, God also sees to it that the powers acquired by such qualifications are used only for the welfare of mankind.

The moment, one uses them for immoral purpose, the extraordinary faculties given by God become the cause of ones own destruction.

Acquiring this extraordinary boon, Bhasmasur became very egoistic.

He thought, if with this extraordinary power he killed Shiva, there would be none left after him to grant this boon to others He decided to destroy Shiva by placing his hand on the head of Shiva.

Shiva is known to honor his word. Bhasmasur knew that for keeping the sanctity of his word, Shiva would not save himself and thus he will become like the Almighty and own Goddess Parvati too.

However, no thought remains secret from God.

The moment this immoral thought occurred to Bhasmasur, God devised a plan to make Bhasmasur destroy his own self with his own extraordinary power.

God created a clone, looking exactly like Parvati.

This double of Parvati approached Bhasmasur and agreed to marry him on the condition that he learnt to dance in her style.

Bhasmasur readily agreed to her proposal and asked her to teach him dancing in her style. The double of Parvati asked him to imitate her postures during the dance.

While the clone Parvati danced, Bhasmasur began to imitate her each posture. In course of dancing, the double of Parvati casually placed her hand on her own head.

In his excitement and anticipation of having Parvati as his wife, Bhasmasur forgot about the power given by God. Imitating the teacher, he also kept his hand on his own head and was burnt to ashes.

MORAL
An extraordinary talent should be regarded as a special gift of God for service of mankind. When a talent or extraordinary position in society is used immorally or for one's own vested interest, avarice or ego, it ultimately becomes the cause of one's own downfall.

Anger Distorts
the Capacity to Think

*B*y practicing rigorous asceticism and devout yoga sadhana, Durvasa had achieved the status of a rishi (sage). However, he could not give up the habit of losing temper on small issues. He often became angry with people on their minor faults.

when anger becomes a habit it sees no reason.

When Durvasa got angry he cursed the person who had made him angry. As he had developed supernatural powers of a rishi, whatever he said happened. His curse frequently made people miserable. People were afraid to face him.

Once in the course of his visit to King Ambrish's court, Durvasa became annoyed with the king.

The king had not done any wrong. Nor did he show any disrespect to Durvasa. But somehow, some minor

35

mistake or some thing in his court had made Durvasa angry.

(As such, when anger becomes a habit it sees no reason).

The displeasure of Durvasa made Ambrish apprehensive of his curse.

Ambrish was a great devotee of Vishnu. In order to escape the curse of the rishi, he began to pray.

Ambrish was an honest king who cared for the people in his empire. Hearing his sincere prayer, Vishnu decided to protect him. He launched his Sudarshan Chakra (an unflinching omnipotent divine weapon) to chase Durvasa away from Ambrish.

Finding the Sudarshan Chakra coming towards him, Durvasa ran and ran to escape it. However, as only Vishnu had the power to call the Sudarshan Chakra back, Durvasa was left with no alternative but to apologize to Vishnu for making his devotee unhappy.

MORAL

One who troubles a devotee of God invites wrath of God.

Bad consequences of anger should be taken as punishment by God.

One should control one's temper.

The Reward for
Speaking Truth

Great people are very truthful since their childhood. When Mahatma Gandhi was a small child, he was never late in reaching school. Though he did not have a watch or clock with him, he would guess the time by looking at the position of the sun in the sky.

One day the sky was overcast with clouds and it began to rain. Gandhi did not care getting drenched by the rain. However because of the clouds in the sky, he could not guess the time of the day.

That day he was late in reaching his school.

The principal of the school was very strict. He asked Gandhi about the reason for coming late. Gandhi told him the truth, but the principal did not believe him.

The principal fined him for arriving late. It made Gandhi weep.

His friend asked, "Why are you weeping for such a small punishment".

Gandhi replied, "I am not crying because I have been fined. I feel hurt, because the principal thought that I was lying.

I always speak truth. No one has ever accused me of lying."

When the principal came to know, why Gandhi cried, he called him to his office and praised him for his courage of speaking truth. He returned back the fine saying it was a reward for his truthfulness.

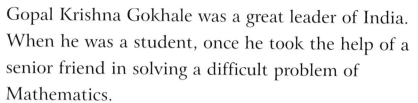

Gopal Krishna Gokhale was a great leader of India. When he was a student, once he took the help of a senior friend in solving a difficult problem of Mathematics.

The teacher thought that Gokhle had himself solved the problem. He praised him in the class and also rewarded him.

However, instead of being happy, Gokhale began to cry. When the teacher asked him the reason, he told him that he had taken the help of a student in solving the problem.

His truthfulness very much impressed the teacher. He said, "You need not return the reward. Take it as a reward for your truthfulness.

MORAL

The value of truth is greater than any loss.

39

Real Happiness
Lies in Helping Others

During his stay in America Swami Vivekananda generally cooked his own meals. When there were other persons around in his house during mealtime, Swami Ji first served food to his guests before taking meals.

One day when Vivekananda was about to take his meals, a group of boys rang the bell.

Welcoming the children in, swami ji enquired whether they had taken their meals?

The boys told him that they had not eaten anything and were feeling hungry. Vivekananda asked the boys to take meals at his house.

However, because he had prepared the food for himself only, nothing was left for him after the guests had eaten.

Nevertheless, Vivekananda appeared very happy and satisfied.

An American lady, present in his house at that time was surprised at the reaction of Vivekananda.

She queried, "When there was not sufficient food, why did you invite the boys to take food at your house?"

Vivekananda replied, "The need of the soul is greater than the hunger of the body.

If I had taken meals myself, while there were hungry persons around me, my soul would never have forgiven me for my selfishness. By feeding these hungry children, I satisfied the hunger of my soul.

The memory of satisfaction on the faces of these hungry children after they had taken meals will always make me happy.

Insults or Praise do not Affect
Great Men

S wami Ramkrishna Paramhansa was a renowned saint of India. Though he never wrote a book, his preaching have enlightened and changed life of millions of men and women. The writings of his disciple, Swami Vivekananda continue to be a source of inspiration for mankind around the world.

Swami Ramkrishna Paramhansa was a person of very simple living habits. Because of his simple clothes and child-like innocence people often failed to recognize his greatness.

Dr. Mahendra Nath Sarkar was a famous, rich physician of Calcutta. He had heard about the saintliness of Ramkrishna and was eager to meet him.

One day he paid a visit to his hermitage.

Swami Ramkrishna was seated in meditation in a garden in front of his hutment. Seeing his simple clothes, Dr. Mahendra got the impression that he was a gardener employed by the saint.

Enlightened persons do not value material gifts.

It is a tradition in India to carry some token of respect while paying a visit to a sage.

Enlightened persons do not value material gifts.

Hence, devotees offer them flowers.

Dr. Mahendra thought, that, on meeting Ramkrishna, he should offer him a flower.

Thinking that the simple looking man sitting in the garden before him was a gardener of Ramkrishna, he called him by a gesture. Pointing at a flower he asked him to pick the flower for

him. Swami ji quietly got up and picking the flower, politely handed it over to Dr. Mahendra and walked back into his hut.

Later, Dr. Mahendra entered the hut to meet Swami ji, he was taken aback by seeing that the person whom he had asked to pick the flower himself was the saint.

He felt very embarrassed and sincerely apologized for his mistake.

However, Swami ji had taken the incident very casually. Saintly souls never feel offended by anyone. He did not speak a word about the incident.

Personal appearances of great men are often misleading. Simple living, absence of pride and humility in behavior are signs of greatness.

MORAL

Great personalities prefer simple living and high thinking. Praise or insults do not affect them. They are calm, happy and merciful in all circumstances.

Practice Makes One
Perfect

A student was very weak in his studies. He was very dull and repeatedly failed in his school examinations. His classmates teased him for his foolishness. Wherever he went, people made fun of him.

One day, feeling very unhappy, he decided to run away from his home. After walking for some distance, he got tired and sat besides a well for taking rest.

While he was brooding about his unfortunate life, a deep groove on the hard rock on the rim of the well caught his attention.

He wondered how such a hard rock had developed the depression? While he was thinking about it, a woman came to the well to draw water.

Tying a rope on the handle of a bucket, she threw it in the well and began to pull up the bucket filled with water.

The boy noticed, that while she pulled up the bucket, the rope tied to the bucket rubbed in the groove on the rock. He understood, that it was the rope rubbing against the rock that had created the groove in the rock.

He noticed that though the rope was much softer than the rock, it could cut through the hard rock by rubbing against it again and again.

He had found the solution to his problem of failures in examinations.

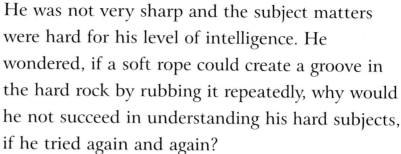

He was not very sharp and the subject matters were hard for his level of intelligence. He wondered, if a soft rope could create a groove in the hard rock by rubbing it repeatedly, why would he not succeed in understanding his hard subjects, if he tried again and again?

Abandoning the thought of going away, he returned back to his home and began to work hard for his studies with greater enthusiasm.

Now things had changed. He began to enjoy reading and gradually became more meticulous and thorough in his studies.

Eventually, he became renowned as a great scholar. This is the true story of Varadraj, who is well known for his famous Sanskrit Grammar treatise called "Kaumudi Siddhanta".

MORAL

Nothing is impossible to achieve if there is a will, hard work and perseverance in effort.

47

The Secret
of Vijaya's Rise

Two sisters Vijaya and Jaya were students of the same class in the school. Jaya was only one year older than Vijaya. Their parents loved both of them very much and treated them equally.

The two sisters had similar likes and dislikes. They celebrated their birth anniversaries together on the same day and had common friends in the neighborhood. They loved each other very much.

They never quarreled or complained about each other to their parents.

However, whereas the younger sister Vijaya had many friends in the school, Jaya found it difficult to create friendship even with her classmates. The teachers too showered praise on Vijaya and hardly ever paid attention to the elder sister Jaya.

On the annual day of the school, Vijaya was declared as the best and most popular student.

It made Jaya unhappy. She could not understand in what way she was inferior to Vijaya. She also wondered why her younger sister was more popular than her.

One day she asked this to their mother.

She said, "Mom! I try to be as friendly to everyone as Vijaya but the teachers and students of the school have chosen her as the most popular girl. Why people like Vijaya more than me? Is it because she is more attractive than me?"

Her mother replied, "No dear, you are as beautiful as Vijaya. However Vijaya has learnt certain ways of doing things, which has made her more liked than you. She has adopted the qualities of good manners, obedience and duty-consciousness.

Have you ever found Vijaya speaking loudly or rudely to anyone?

She is very respectful and polite in her behavior with other persons. She always speaks with a smile on her face. She never quarrels with any fellow student. Nor does she ever complain about anyone.

Because of these good habits, everyone considers her as a friend.

Mother asked Jaya, " Do you know why she is also so popular with the

49

teachers?

There are so many children in the school, that teachers cannot remember everyone. The teachers are attracted towards only those students who are different from others because of some special quality in them. Students having good qualities become teacher's pet.

Jaya asked, "What are the qualities which teachers like in a student?

Mother replied, " You have to form a habit of doing things in a proper way to come in notice of others.

I shall tell you some important things which each student should remember."

1. Cleanliness:

You have to always be neat and tidy. You should be clean and your face should look fresh (alert). Your hands and feet should be properly washed. You

The teachers are attracted towards only those students who are different from others because of some special quality in them. Students having good qualities become teacher's pet.

should have clean teeth. You r smile is attractive only when your teeth are clean.

You should also have neatly groomed hair, properly cut nails. Your school uniform should be spotless, clean and creaseless.

Unless you are sick, taking bath daily is absolutely necessary. Nobody likes to stay near a dirty person. People avoid dirty persons. If you associate with dirty persons, you fall sick frequently.

Would you like to sit in the class besides the student, who is dirty and smelling foul ?

For keeping good health, it is also necessary to keep one's personal articles, clothes and place of living clean.

The things you eat should also be clean and fresh. Items of food prepared and kept uncovered become dirty. Dust and flies pollute such foodstuff with germs of disease; children, who eat such food, frequently become sick.

The things you eat should also be clean and fresh. Items of food prepared and kept uncovered become dirty. Dust and flies pollute such foodstuff with germs of disease; children, who eat such food, frequently become sick.

2. Punctuality and regularity of daily routine:

Teachers like those children who are never late in coming to school. The children, who watch television shows till late hours in the night, cannot getup early in the morning. As a result, they often have difficulty in leaving the bed early in the morning. For reaching the school in time they take their breakfast and pack their schoolbag hurriedly. Because of hurry they often forget to take books and exercise-books according to their timetable and face punishment in the school.

Going to bed late in the night and getting up early for school also does not give them enough time for homework and sufficient sleep for rest.

In the classroom, they feel drowsy and cannot concentrate on the subject being taught.

Teachers do not like students who are sleepy in the classroom.

Hence for being alert and attentive in the classroom, it is necessary to have a proper timetable for studying, playing, entertainment and going to bed.

For obtaining good marks in the examinations it is also necessary to have a routine of regular study. Only those students can maintain the schedule of good studies who go to bed early in the night and get up early in the morning.

Students, who top in their class, have a habit of studying regularly at home. They prepare their lessons in advance.

It gives them an opportunity to revise the lesson, when it is being taught in the school. It keeps them ahead of other students.

3. Discipline:

Teachers love students who maintain discipline in the school and classroom.

Teachers do not like noisy and quarrelsome students or those who always keep on complaining about something or the other.

A good student should always avoid company of such persons who have the habit of criticizing others.

It is not good to have company of children who have a habit of telling bad things about others. Remember!

Those who have the habit of criticizing others will also talk bad about you to others behind your back.

It is a bad habit to talk during the class.

Jaya asked, "Why is it necessary to keep quiet in the classroom?

Mother replied, " While talking during the class, you learn nothing.

You can do one thing at a time. You can either talk or listen. When the teacher is speaking, you cannot talk and simultaneously listen to the teacher. Because of the noise made by you while talking, other students too cannot listen to the teacher properly.

You might have noticed that talkative students are generally not good in their studies.

Only by keeping quiet and being attentive in the classroom you can concentrate on the subject being taught.

Unless you are attentive, how can you find out what you have not understood? How can you ask the teacher for clarifications?"

Jaya said, "Mom! Now I have understood the secret of Vijaya's success. I shall also practise these good habits".

MORAL

Cleanliness, punctuality, regularity in routine, discipline and modesty are necessary for winning friends and influencing people.

Four Principles
of Success of Great Persons

For Success in Life:

1. Discipline in behavior

2. Discipline in using available resources

3. Discipline in using time

4. Discipline in thinking

Shreya is a student of high school. She desires to be successful and famous in life when she grows up. She believes that only those persons became successful in life who had better opportunities.

Shreya often wonders why God provides opportunities only to a selected few persons? Does God favor some and overlook others? Is she going to get opportunities for success or not?

Shreya's uncle is in the board of directors of a big company. He is counted among very successful persons of the city. One day Shreya went to meet him and asked about the secrets of success in life. Her younger sister Sumedha also accompanied her.

Shreya: Uncle! Is it possible for everyone to have opportunities to achieve higher goals in life?

Uncle: "Opportunities are available at every moment in life. One who identifies them and steps forward to use them becomes successful.

Opportunities are like candles. Suppose you are in a dark room. There is a matchbox and a candle in your house, but unless you know where it is kept and how to light it, these are useless for you. You will remain in darkness in spite of having means of lighting around you.

On the other hand, the person who knows where the matchbox and the candle are kept and also knows how to light them will have no problem.

As a person learns lighting a matchbox at an early age, great men had learn the basic principles for identifying and making best use of opportunities from their very childhood.

Shreya: Sir please tell me about these principles.

Uncle: There are four basic principles for success in life:
1. Discipline in behavior
2. Discipline in using available resources
3. Discipline in using time
4. Discipline in thinking

Sumedha: How does one learn the discipline in behavior?

Uncle: Human behavior depends mainly on habits of three parts of body. These are tongue, eyes and ears. These are required to be trained to work under discipline.

The tongue has two functions: One, It is used for speaking; and Two, It enables one to get taste of food.

Let me first tell you about the effect of speech on people.

For success in any work, you need some supporters, admirers and associates. You must know how to make friends and influence people. If you make enemies in life, you get none of these.

You make friends or enemies by your habits of speaking.

The most important thing to remember is to refrain from criticizing and back-biting. With these habits you create enemies and people begin to distrust you.

You should also never speak in anger or in an insulting way.

When you speak in anger or insult somebody, the other person also replies back in the same way. Thus begins a tournament of angry words, at the end of which no one wins. In most cases, both the persons who are engaged in exchange of angry words remember them for a long time. Both wait for an opportunity for revenge.

By criticizing, backbiting and quarreling too one makes many enemies.

Never believe any one talking against the action of another person, without verifying the facts yourself. For their own selfish interests, people often speak lies and create enmity amongst friends.

Such enemies, created by your own self, neither help nor admire your work. On the contrary, they look for opportunities

to create obstacles in your success. On the contrary, by being polite in speech you make many friends, who come to your help, whenever you take up some difficult work.

Shreya: What shall we do if someone makes us angry ?

Uncle: Do you know why someone gets angry?

One loses temper, when something happens against his wishes.

Sometimes people also lose temper because they are tired, or they had had a confrontation with someone earlier.

There are simple ways to calm down an angry person.

One: Never contradict an angry person.

While facing an angry person keep quiet or get away from him. Nobody can remain angry for a long time, when none else is speaking.

Two: At that moment when someone is angry, accept whatever is being said. Later, when the anger cools down, you may explain your viewpoint in detail.

Three: Sometimes you can calm down tempers by telling a joke. One cannot remain angry and laugh at the same time.

Now I will tell you about the second discipline of tongue.

Besides speaking, the tongue has one more vital function. It is also used to feel the taste of food or liquid.

But greed of tongue or harmful habit of taste spoils one's health and weakens one's mental firmness too.

You should be very careful in choosing the type and quantity of your food and drinks. Everyone knows that habit of taking too much of sweet, spicy foods and fast foods are injurious for health.

The ill effects of smoking, tobacco, hard (alcoholic) drinks and drug addiction are also very well known.

Shreya: Why in spite of knowing that these things are not good for health people develop the habit of taking these things.

Uncle: Taste and thrill of such things, if repeated without any check, develops into a habit.

Initially one tastes something out of curiosity. Sometimes other persons also persuade a friend or an acquaintance to taste some 'exotic' food, drink or smoke. No one likes the first puff of a cigarette, the initial taste of tobacco or the first peg of hard drink. But by tasting again and again a habit is formed and the person becomes a slave to the habit.

Once a habit is formed, the thing being consumed becomes a necessity. Then this necessity becomes an addiction.

One cannot live without consuming the thing irrespective of knowing that it is harmful for health.

Hence, the company of those persons who have bad habits should be strictly avoided. Never taste something, which is known to be injurious for health, even out of curiosity.

So far we have discussed how the proper habits of speaking and consuming the

right food or drink help in maintaining the discipline of body.

Sumedha: "Mother tells me that one should have a discipline in food habits as well."

Uncle: "Yes! If you form a habit of frequently eating sweet, spicy or junk food, or consuming soft drinks you may eat or drink even when your body does not require it.

When the body requires food or water, it naturally makes you feel hungry or thirsty. Consuming food in absence of hunger, spoils digestion, makes man over weighted, and he falls sick frequently.

Shreya: "You told about the discipline of sight. How can looking at things influence other persons?

Uncle: "Apart from the voice, choice of words and style of speaking, what influences people significantly are the eyes of the speaker".

Eyes are like mirrors of mind and heart. Whatever you think or feel is also conveyed through your eyes. Feelings are expressed through eyes. Eyes convey love and hate, happiness and sadness, anger and mercy.

A lover conveys love while looking into the eyes of the loved one. One pleading for mercy looks straight into the eyes.

The eyes betray what a person is trying to hide by words or some gestures.

A liar avoids looking into the eyes of the questioner. Persons who have the habit of frequently looking here and there are not trusted.

Sight has a great power of influencing people during communication. That is why speakers, persons being interviewed and artists performing on stage are asked to look into the eyes of persons facing them.

A few examples from history will illustrate the influencing power of sight.

The dreaded dacoit Angulimal could not face Gautam Buddha because of latter's power of sight and became his disciple.

It is well known, that while speaking to Mahatma Gandhi, if the political opponents looked into his eyes, they unknowingly agreed to his views.

Saints transform ordinary persons into great men by transmitting their spiritual energy (Shaktipat), by looking into their eyes.

Sumedha: Sir! Could you tell me how to develop the power of sight?

Uncle: God has given everyone the capacity to develop the power of sight. It can be developed by some special yogic exercises like 'Tratak' or 'Bindu Yoga'.

However, for children it is sufficient to avoid looking at bad things and purify the sight by looking at beautiful, good, things of Nature.

We make the power of sight weak by looking at bad things. We must not look at sinful acts. Whatever we see stays in our subconscious mind and influences our activities sometime or the other.

If you see again and again, someone wearing indecent clothes or behaving in a vulgar way, you may become tempted

to wear similar clothes or behave in the same manner.

Frequently watching people smoking, taking drugs or gambling may tempt you to do the same thing and eventually make you an addict.

On the contrary, if you see only activities of good people or read about them, you will be motivated to do virtuous things and the power of influencing will increase in your sight.

There is a story in Mahabharata about Gandhari, the mother of Duryodhan.

Gandhari had kept her eyes blind-folded for years. Because of not viewing evil or having diversions and unnecessary attractions, for a long time, her sight had developed a great power. So she could make the body of his son Duryodhan, invincible, by looking at it.

Shreya: Uncle, I did not know that our own speaking, eating and seeing has so much effect on other persons. In future, I shall be careful about these things.

Sumedha: My classmate Mahesh speaks very sweetly. He never criticizes or insults anyone. We never find him speaking in anger or using bad words. Everyone likes him. Yet his parents do not give him any responsibility for work. Why is it so?

Uncle: For managing things, simply being sweet in speech does not help. Perhaps, your friend Mahesh does not know how to use his personal articles properly?

Unless one learns to keep articles of personal use systematically, no one believes that the person is responsible.

Shreya: One day I went to meet Mahesh at his house and found his things scattered allover his room. His mother told me that he does not keep his school-bag, books, clothes, sport tools and toys at proper place. Whenever he needs something, he wastes a lot of time in searching and becomes late for school.

Systematic arrangement of articles of personal use is the first lesson to be learnt for management. Articles should be treated like study-notes for examination. Unless kept properly and taken care of regularly, these are not available when required.

Keeping things in a disorderly manner also does not create a good impression on an onlooker. Dirty, haphazardly kept, broken, non-usable articles show that the owner is a careless person. No one trusts such a person for a responsible work.

Uncle: Not only keeping things systematically, their proper utilization is also necessary for success.

There are two important things to be learnt about management of articles.

One: Only those things should be acquired which are absolutely necessary.

Two: Things should be used without any wastage. People waste a lot of time and money in acquiring unnecessary things, simply because these are latest in trend or because someone else have them.

If an old article is usable there is no point in having another new one for the same purpose?

Whatever things are available for any work should also be carefully used without any wastage.

For example, if you continue to wear your new clothes daily, these will get faded or worn out and you will have nothing to wear for special occasions.

Similarly, money should not be wasted in unnecessary expenditure. One must know when, for what purpose and how and how much to spend.

Only those persons, who know how to keep and use things systematically and use the available money in a wise manner, are given opportunities and resources to do great things.

By gradually taking responsibilities for greater and greater work and proving one's worth, one gains confidence and experience.

Experience is acquired by learning from childhood itself. Therefore one should not shirk from taking responsibility for any work, however small it is. Each and every work, big or small should be carried out with full enthusiasm, concentration, without caring for tiredness.

This is a great secret of success for everything in life.

Sumedha: Uncle! You also mentioned about 'Discipline of time'? How does one learn to discipline one's time?

Uncle: God has given the same time to everyone for working. The great people of the world have the same time available to them during a day that you and I have.

Whether it is a child or adult, boy or girl, man or woman poor or rich, an ordinary citizen or the prime minister of India; everyone has the same seven days in week, thirty days in a month and 365 days in a year.

Shreya: When everyone has the same time, why some persons become successful in life and others do not?

Uncle: Only those persons become successful in life, who know how to use their time?

Time is the most valuable thing in life. Not a single moment should be wasted in gossiping and criticizing or quarrelling. Every moment should be utilized in some constructive activity or in learning new things which can be helpful to people.

Great men and women had learnt the secret of proper utilization of time during their early childhood. They had no time to think about entertainment, gossip, and mischief, criticism, backbiting or quarrelling.

A lot of time is also wasted in decoration of body to impress others. Although it is necessary to be clean and neatly dressed, it is useless to spend too much time in worrying about clothes, footwear, fashion, ornaments. Time spent in sleep, entertainment and lousiness should also be carefully controlled.

Discipline of time also means having a fixed, regular routine. People, who are

not punctual or have the habit of postponing work, waste their own as well as other's time. Those who waste time do not have time for doing great things in life.

Whereas wise, intelligent persons use all of their time for increasing their qualifications by learning new things. It gives them opportunities to do great things in life.

The discipline of time has to be practised since childhood itself.

Sumedha: Uncle! You talked about the discipline of thinking. How does it help one in success?

Uncle: You have asked a very good question.

How you behave and everything you do depend upon what you think. If you are habituated to thinking of helping others, you will immediately step forward to help a person in need. But, if your thoughts are wicked, you will tend only harm others by your activities.

Your thoughts also make you chose good or bad company. When you make friends with good people in life, they will give you good advice and help you in need without any selfish interest. It will bring you success in life.

Wrong thinking will bring you to bad selfish persons, who will outwardly flatter you as true friends, but will stay with you only for their own selfish interest. Similarly, dirty thoughts will spoil your character.

Shreya: How does one know what is right or wrong thinking?

Uncle: It is easy to know whether you are thinking right or wrong.

If your thoughts result in activities, which help someone physically or mentally, you are doing right thinking.

On the contrary, if your thinking is likely to harm or hurt somebody, your thinking is wrong and harmful for your physical and mental health.

However, like every other thing in life, the habit of mindful, good and thorough thinking is also to be cultivated from childhood itself.

Sumedha: How can one develop the habit of proper thinking?

Uncle: For developing the habit of right thinking, you have to seek the company of right thinking persons, read only such books which give you right thoughts and take part only in those activities which are helpful to others. All men who became great had worked in some field or the other for the welfare of society.

For cultivating right thoughts, it is also necessary to have belief in God. The thought that God is Omnipresent will not let you think of doing any wrong, in any circumstance, wherever you are? The thought that God is the eternal Light of Virtues, with enlighten your mind.

Learning to think rightly also requires contemplation on good thoughts and creative practice. That is why musicians, sports persons and soldiers have regular practice sessions.

Righteous thinking can also be cultivated by forming a habit of reading some literature on morality daily. One way is to read the enlightening scriptures or biographies of great people.

Shreya: We have understood that for being successful in life one must adopt four disciplines: the discipline in behavior; the discipline in using available things; discipline in using available time and discipline in thinking.

Sumedha: Uncle! We are so thankful to you for telling us these secrets of success, which made people renowned in the world.

MORAL

Experience is acquired by learning from childhood itself. Therefore one should not shirk from taking responsibility for any work, however small it is. Each and every work, big or small should be carried out with full enthusiasm, concentration, without caring for